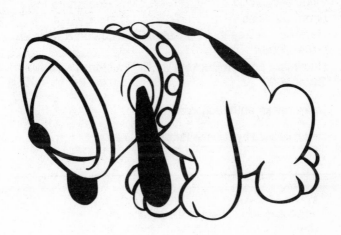

A Dog's Life

ℛ
RAVETTE PUBLISHING

Originally published by HarperCollins Publishers Ltd
under the titles:
Hackman: A Dog in a Bucket © Bill Houston & Michael
Grant 2005
Hackman: Love in Buckets © Bill Houston & Michael
Grant 2006

(www.hackmanthedog.com)

First published by Ravette Publishing 2009.

Printed in the UK by CPI Bookmarque, Croydon, CR0 4TD
for Ravette Publishing Limited,
PO Box 876
Horsham
West Sussex RH12 9GH

ISBN: 978-1-84161-315-4

Hackman!
a dog in a bucket!

Hackman, or 'Hack' to his friends, family and shrink, is very set in his ways. Rarely stuck for an answer, he feels he has a Sgt. Bilko rapier-like wit but deep down, he's as insecure as the rest of us. He worries about being laughed at and assumes he's part of a 'con' before it happens.

This gives him a very blinkered view of life ... and the bucket doesn't help either.

His persistent 'medical problem' means the continual wearing of his 'bucket' and leads to constant visits to a pet shrink of dubious repute.

Follow his hilarious adventures in our first two pocket books and get a rare insight into the messed up world of this adorable bucket-wearing spaniel.

©Bill Houston & Michael Grant Yorto Licensing 2005

©Bill Houston & Michael Grant Yarto Licensing 2005

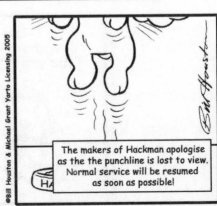

The makers of Hackman apologise as the the punchline is lost to view. Normal service will be resumed as soon as possible!

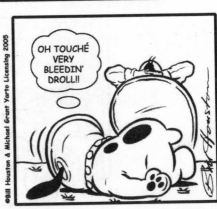

If you enjoyed this book you'll be pleased to know
the second book in the series is also available at
your local bookshop or direct from the publisher at
the address below.